85p.
IN UK ONLY

SBN 361 02848 2
"The 'Sooty' Book Series" by arrangement with Harry Corbett.
Approved by Sooty Concessions Limited and Sooty Overseas Limited
and Licensed under Trade Mark rights.
Made and printed in Great Britain by Purnell & Sons Ltd.,
Paulton (Somerset) and London.

Purnell

Sooty's
Annual

A Magic Ride

Kipper, Butch and Sooty went to catch a railway train.
"We've missed it!" Kipper panted, as they all charged up the lane.

"I'll use this stick to help," said Sooty. "Sit astride it, please."
The whizzy stick was magic, so it raced the train with ease!

Sooty on his Own

1. Sooty likes making lots of noise! Once he thought he would make lots of musical noises. So he got out his box of musical toys. "Which one shall I play first?" he thought to himself.

2. The little bear chose a trombone. "This should make quite a din," he chuckled, as he raised the mouthpiece to his lips and blew into it. The trombone made a *very* nice din!

3. Trombones have a slidy bit which slides in and out. When Sooty slid the slide – CRASH! He knocked over a clock. "Oh," said Sooty, "perhaps I'd better try a less crashy instrument."

4. Sooty tried playing a saxophone and a trumpet both at once. But it was not easy to make more than an *eeeky* squeak come out of both of them. "I'll try something else," Sooty thought.

5. The bear really enjoyed playing the guitar! But as it was such a small one, the twangy noise that it made was really rather a quiet one, and Sooty wanted an extra-noisy noise.

6. It was then that Sooty found the drum in his musical toy box. "It's rather small," he smiled, "but I think it will make a BIG noise by the time I've worked some *Izzy-whizzy* magic."

7. What Sooty did next was not very magic at all. He stood between two mirrors so that he could see quite a few Sootys with quite a few drums. *Then* he got out his magic wand.

8. *Twizzle!* When the magic started to work, all the reflections of Sooty came to life. It was an amazing sight. "That's just the first part of my idea," grinned Sooty. "Now for the best part."

9. Bang, bong, bonkity-BOOM! Just a few seconds later, Sooty asked all those Sooty Drummers to start drumming. What a wonderful lot of musical noise all those Sooty Drummers made!

10. They crashed and banged away until even Sooty had had enough. "It's fun being the leader of a drum band," beamed the delighted bear. "I must give all my friends a Drum Concert soon!"

Two Funny Freezy Pages

1. What an *enormous* block of ice cream this seems to be. But really it is just an ordinary-sized one, and Sooty has used his magic to make himself and Sweep and Soo small, so that they can ski on it! "Is it Soo or Sweep whose path leads to the winning flag?" asks Sooty. "*Do* find out—ready, steady, GO!"

2. These ice creams have their flavours written below them, but the letters have been jumbled up. Can you work out what the flavours are?

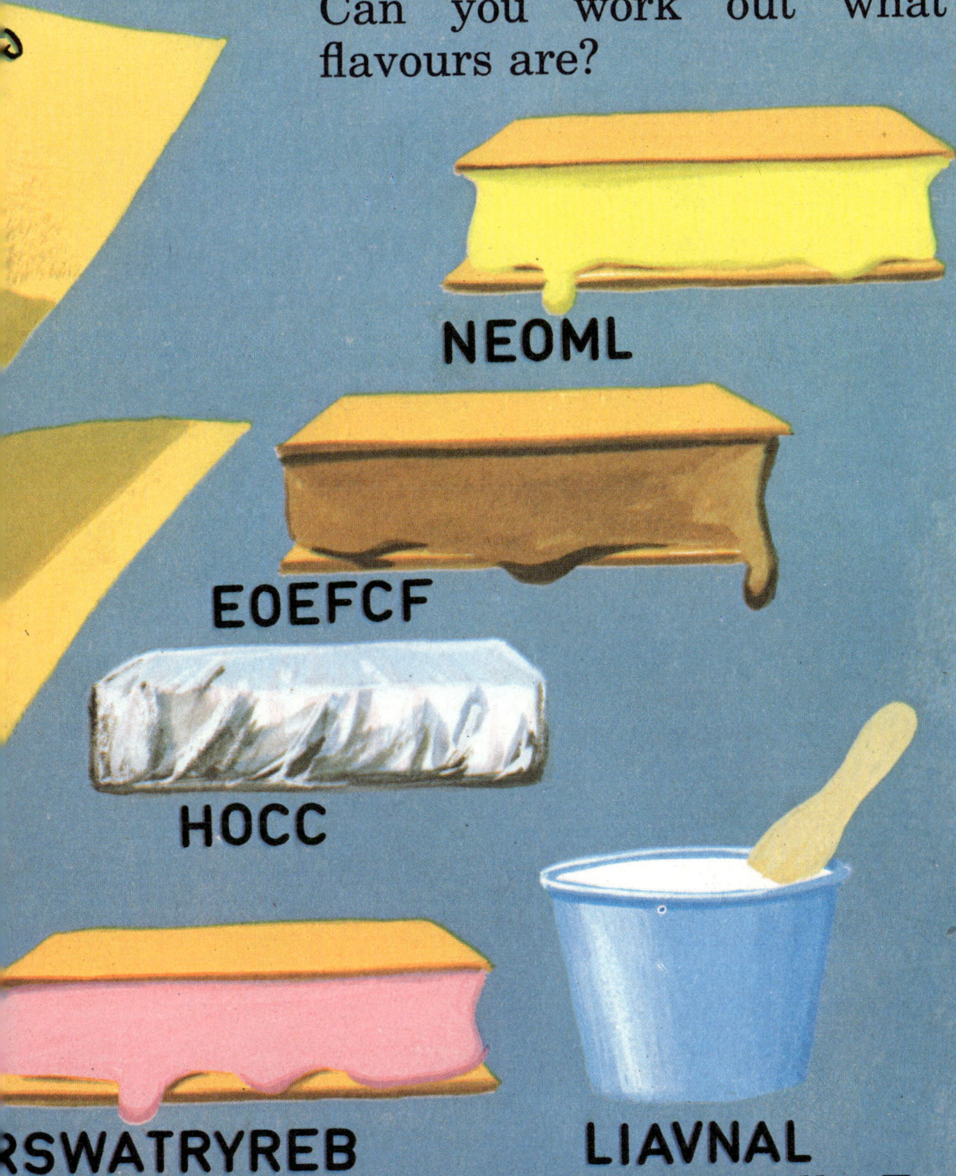

3. Just look at Sooty's magic Lolly Tree. Carefully count all the lollies you can see. Some of them are Lime, some are Orange, and some are browny Cola. Write in the numbers in the "empty" lollies below, then add up *all* the lollies!

(1) Soo's snowy path leads to the winning flag. (2) The names are CHOC, LEMON, COFFEE, VANILLA, and STRAWBERRY. (3) There are 4 Lime lollies, 5 Orange lollies, and 6 Cola lollies. These add up to 15 lollies in all.

Jumble Day!

SWEEP and Sooty just can't resist buying bargains at Jumble Sales. They have just been to a *wonderful* Jumble Sale, and bought all sorts of things, as you can see.

"All the things we have bought are different," laughs Sweep. "But one of them is different from the others in a different sort of way," adds Sooty. "Look at everything we have bought with sharp eyes—*and* at three of them which are hidden in this funny picture—and see if YOU can see which is the *different* different one."

The drum is the different thing. All the other things have names which begin with the letter T.

The Pantomime Adventure

SOOTY AND SWEEP were in such a hurry!

"You're taking *ages* to put your coat on, Sooty," said Sweep, as they stood in the hall of Sooty's house. "I'm doing it as fast as I can," replied Sooty. "There, it's done! Off we go to the show!"

The show was an exciting pantomime.

If *you* had been standing in the street near Sooty's house that afternoon, you would have seen the two friends simply *dashing* down the pavement, across the zebra crossing extra-carefully, along past the new self-service garage, and around the corner to the Sootyville Theatre.

The friends were simply *longing* to see the pantomime which was on there.

It was all about a boy in faraway China who found a magic lamp. When he rubbed the lamp, a magic person called a genie appeared. Do you know that boy's name? Yes, it was Aladdin.

Families were thronging into the theatre by the time Sweep and Sooty got there, and Sweep and Sooty had to make their way past lots of chattering children to reach the little office where the tickets for the show were being sold.

"Two seats for today's show, please!" said Sooty, when he found himself facing the ticket lady behind the window.

The ticket lady looked up in surprise.

"Not for *today,* love, surely?" she said.

"Yes, two of the very best seats you have!" grinned Sweep over Sooty's shoulder.

"But all the seats for today's show – and tomorrow's – were sold weeks ago," replied the lady. "I'm awfully sorry,

Sooty. It's such a popular show. People do sometimes bring back tickets they can't use, at the last moment. Would you like to wait and see if any of these turn up?"

Poor Sooty and Sweep. They were so disappointed. They just turned away sadly from the ticket office. "She's right, of course," sighed Sooty. "We should have booked our tickets long ago—I suppose we'll SEE THE SHOW AFTER ALL!"

Sweep looked at Sooty in astonishment. "What do you mean, *see the show after all,* Sooty?" he said. "I thought that . . ."

". . . I thought that I'd have a good idea if I *tried* to have one," beamed Sooty. "So I tried hard, and I've had a *splendid* idea. Come with me!"

Sooty led the puzzled Sweep to the front of the theatre where there was a large *Aladdin* poster advertising the pantomime.

"Stand right in front of the poster," smiled Sooty. "It may not be quite the same show as this one we are going to see, but we *are* going to see Aladdin."

From his pocket, Sooty took his very own magic wand. With it he can do all sorts of amazingly magic things. *"Izzy-whizzy, let's get busy—let's have a happy time in the land of pantomime!"* he chuckled.

Magic sparks fizzled and twizzled magically at the end of Sooty's wand.

"Jump!" called Sooty. And taking the pup's hand, Sooty jumped up at the poster—and right through it!

The friends did not find themselves on the other side of the poster. They found themselves standing next to Aladdin himself!

"Welcome to our land, merry people!" smiled Aladdin, bowing low. "May your stay here be a happy one!"

"Er, I'm sure it will be, Master Aladdin," said Sweep, who never quite gets used to Sooty's magic tricks. "Just look at that lamp he's carrying—it must be the magic one," Sweep whispered to Sooty.

"Perhaps you would like to see the wonderful cave where chests of jewels sparkle and glitter, young sirs," Aladdin went on. "Ooh, yes please," beamed Sooty. "Do take us there."

Along twisty streets, past Eastern shops and houses walked Sooty and Sweep, with Aladdin as their guide.

Sweep was going to ask Aladdin if *he* could carry the lamp, when suddenly the lamp was snatched from Aladdin's hand. Sooty and Sweep just had time to see a stern-looking man with a black beard holding that lamp before he dashed off around the corner.

"That was a man who calls himself my uncle!" gasped Aladdin. "He has tried to steal the lamp before. Please will you help me get it back, good friends?"

"We certainly will!" cried Sooty and Sweep together, and the three of them scampered after the man with the lamp just as fast as they could.

"It's no use, we'll never be able to catch him up," gasped Aladdin after a few seconds. "Without the lamp, I am powerless to work any magic to help us, too!"

Sooty's answer was to take out his magic wand and whisper an *Izzy-whizzy* magic spell. A few seconds later than that, Sweep, Aladdin and Sooty were all *flying* through the air like birds, and catching up with the thief very speedily.

"Your magic is most excellent!" shouted Aladdin to Sooty. "We will soon have the lamp back now!"

But when the man saw what was happening, he stopped. Swiftly he rubbed the lamp. Sooty's and Sweep's eyes grew round and wide to see the genie appear! Their eyes grew even wider and rounder when Aladdin's uncle *disappeared*.

The three fliers landed in front of the fierce-looking genie.

"The master of the lamp has

commanded me to send him to a secret hiding place," said the genie in a stern voice. He did not notice Sooty holding his magic wand behind his back and making a very quiet wish. *"Izzy whizzy, please get busy—make that genie rather dizzy!"* said Sooty to himself in a whisper.

Suddenly the genie burst out laughing. He laughed and chuckled and roared with laughter, holding his shaking sides with his huge hands. He laughed so much that even the others had to join in.

"Ho, ho, HO!" he bellowed, "I've laughed so much I feel dizzy! Wouldn't one of you like just one teeny wish to be granted, ha, ha, ho-HO!"

"Send us to the place that uncle has gone to with the lamp," cried Sooty quickly. Before he could say *Abracadabra,* the three friends found themselves in a cave with chests of amazing jewels in it.

"This is the cave you mentioned, Aladdin," gasped Sweep.

"And there's my uncle with the lamp!" replied Aladdin, as a figure hiding behind one of the treasure chests tried to creep to the back of the cave. "I should have guessed he would come here!"

"You are very greedy to want these jewels, and very naughty to take the magic lamp," said Sooty, using *his* magic to make the lamp *whiz* across the cave into his hands. "Now I command the genie of the lamp to transport you and one chest of jewels to the market square, for you to have to sell the jewels there!"

The moment Sooty gave the lamp back to Aladdin, that uncle and a chest crammed

with gems disappeared. And it was in the market place that Aladdin and Sooty and Sweep saw him an hour later, after Aladdin had shown them all the amazing treasure. That uncle was selling wonderful diamonds and emeralds and rubies at the same price that the vegetable man sold carrots, onions, and tomatoes!

"That will teach him to be greedy about jewels!" chuckled Sooty.

"Thank you a thousand times, good friends," smiled Aladdin. "I will long remember your visit here. And now I know it is time for you to return to your country far-

away. Farewell!"

Everything seemed to go *izzily-whizzily* twirly-whirly for Sooty and Sweep then, and they seemed to tumble out of China right back to the ground in front of the theatre.

The ticket office lady was calling to them.

"I've just had two tickets for the show given back to me," she said with a smile. "Would you like to buy them, Sooty?"

"I certainly would like to buy them, please," said he. "We've seen quite a lot of Aladdin, but Sweep and I would like to see *lots* more!"

And into the theatre went the two friends, arm in arm.

Another Pantomime Picture!

SOOTY likes acting in pantomime shows, as well as watching them. Here you can see him and Soo and Sweep in a *very* well-known pantomime. Yes, it is *Cinderella,* and Prince Sooty is trying the crystal shoe on Soo's foot. "I'm sure it's going to fit, so that we can be married and live happily ever, ever after!" cries Sooty. Colour this picture so prettily, won't you?

Sooty's Super Submarine

IT would be *super* to take a trip in Sooty's dear little submarine!

"You *can* come with us and play an exciting game, as well!" Sooty says. The game is a Counters-and-Dice game. Throw a six to start, and follow the instructions if you land on some.

"We're off to visit grand old King Neptune, the king of all the seas," shout Sweep and Sooty. "Let's go!"

1 2 3 4 5 6 7
8
9
10
11 12 13 14 15 16 17 18 19
38 39 40 41 42 43

Hooray for Snow-Fun Day

1. Sooty woke up very bright and very early one wintry morning. "I'll read two stories in my Sooty Annual before I get out of bed," he thought. *Plomp!* Suddenly something flumped floppily onto the window.

2. That something was a snowball! Sooty dashed to the window, and opened it. There was super snow *everywhere*. "Hurry on down and play, or I'll throw *another* snowball!" called Sweep merrily.

3. Sooty got dressed extra quickly. He likes having snowy day fun! While he was putting on his woolly hat, he saw something which gave him an idea for *extra* extra fun. "I'll trick Sweep with those flippers," he chuckled.

4. Once Sooty was outside, he put the flappy underwater flippers on. "I'll make a trail with these, and Sweep will think a funny monster has made it," chuckled the little bear to himself.

5. The footprints that Sooty made were huge ones! "Sweep *will* have a surprise," Sooty thought. But Sooty did not know that Sweep had seen him making those funny monster footprints in the snow.

6. "Sooty won't catch me out with that trick," grinned Sweep, hiding behind a tree. "I'll whiz ahead of him down Oatland Hill, and give *him* the biggest surprise he has ever had, that's what!"

7. So Sweep did just that. Down snowy Oatland Hill whizzed he on his toboggan. Sooty could not see him over the high hedge. But can *you* see what is ahead of swish-down-the-hill Sweep?

8. It was Butch on his tractor, doing a spot of snow clearing in the fields near his farm. Butch didn't see Sweep speeding towards him. But Sweep saw Butch! "Help!" yelled Sweep. "There's going to be a crash!"

9. What a wonderful swerve Sweep swerved. *Swooooosh.* Snow went showering all over Butch and his tractor as the toboggan hurtled past it only inches away. Luckily there were some soft hedges ahead of Sweep.

10. Sweep's crash into the hedges was really quite a nice one. It felt like bumping into lots of candy floss! "I think I'll walk down the hill next time," he thought, as he came to a halt.

11. Just then Sooty came round the corner. It had been hard work walking so far in those flippers. "Yow!" he cried, as he saw what looked like a very big snow monster.

12. The monster was just the snow-covered Butch and his tractor, wasn't it? When the three friends all saw each other, they could not help bursting into laughter.

13. "You two are good at playing tricks on each other," chuckled Butch. "But I've had an idea for something we can all play together. Watch this tractor at work, everyone. It does a grand job."

14. The tractor pushed at the snow, and shoved great piles of it into shapes. "I think I know what Butch is making," grinned Sooty. It was a simply splendid snow castle.

15. What a grand game the three friends had then, taking it in turns to attack the castle. They all agreed that it was the best day in the snow that they could remember.

SOOTY'S DANCING FRIENDS

Four merry friends are dancing
With four merry puppet folk—
Young Sooty *izzy-whizzed* them large,
He did it for a joke.
"The people are from nursery rhymes,"
Laughs Sooty with a grin,
"Now, say which funny nursery rhymes
Those puppet folk are in!"

Sooty is dancing with Little Miss Muffet, Sweep with Little Bo Peep, Ramsbottom with Humpty Dumpty, and Soo with Little Boy Blue.

Kipper and the Kittens

"Look at these five funny kittens on a kennel," says Kipper. "Do you think they all look the same? If you look at them very closely you will see that one of them is not quite the same as all the others."

"I tried to spell the names of these kittens," Kipper smiles, "but I am not very good at spelling, am I? Please tell me what the spelling of all these kittens' names should really be."

"Here are four kittens having a roller-skate ride. They make two exactly-alike pairs," Kipper says. "See how long it takes you to tell which those two exactly-alike kitten pairs are."

(1) Kitten 4 is different. (2) The names should be PIP, SNOWY, FLUFFY, and JET. (3) The pairs are A and C, and B and D.

Sooty Flies to the Moon

RAMSBOTTOM the snake is Sooty Bear's friend. They have lots of fun together when they visit each other, especially when Sooty brings his amazing magic wand with him. For all Sooty has to do to make marvellous magic is to take out his wand, and say *Izzy-whizzy* magic words.

Such wonderful magic happens then!

It was a breezy-bright Saturday morning when Sooty called at Ramsbottom's house. Ramsbottom had invited Sooty over to see a brand-new picture poster he had bought. Sweep, the pup who lives with Sooty, went with him, of course.

Ramsbottom was looking rather *different* when he opened the door to Sweep and Sooty. In fact, Sooty could not see very much of him at all, for he seemed to be covered completely in flappy paper.

"I'm here, behind all this poster," said Ramsbottom's

voice. "This is the poster I was telling you about—it's such a big one I'm not finding it easy to put it up."

The funny snake tried to hurry back across the hall to let his guests in, almost knocking over two vases of flowers as he did so. The poor fellow simply could *not* see where he was going.

Sooty could not help smiling *and* taking something out of his pocket. Can you guess what that something was? It was his magic wand. The helpful bear wanted to help his friend, and he thought the quickest way to do *that* would be a magic way.

"Izzy-whizzy, get busy, please—poster go on wall with ease!" Sooty said.

Shimmery sparks sparkled at the tip of Sooty's wand.

Suddenly the picture poster flew up into the air, whisked around the room like a funny magic carpet, and whizzed towards a wall, sticking there very neatly with a pin in each corner.

The look on Ramsbottom's face was a mixture of surprise and delight!

"Thank you very much, Sooty," he exclaimed. "Now we can all see the poster!"

What an exciting picture poster it was, too. It showed some space travellers, called astronauts, on the Moon, with their space craft next to them.

Sooty and Sweep thought it was the best picture they had seen for ages.

"It must be very thrilling to speed away into the sky and land on the Moon, mustn't it?" sighed Ramsbottom.

"Yes, it must," echoed Sweep.

"You're right!" added Sooty. "So why don't we three do just that?"

"What?" gasped his friends. "How can *we* ever be space flyers?"

Before they could say Space Race backwards, Sooty had waved his magic wand over a small plastic spaceship toy that lay in Ramsbottom's toy box. Already that spaceship was beginning to grow and grow. It grew so quickly that Sooty had to shout: "Please continue now to grow—but out into the garden go!"

In exactly half a minute, a huge spaceship was standing on Ramsbottom's lawn. It was almost as big as Ramsbottom's house. Even Sooty was extra-pleased with the results of his magic.

"What are we waiting for?" he told the others. "Everyone aboard the *Moonship Sooty* for a quick trip to the Moon!"

All three of those friends felt rather strange *swoopy* feelings in their tummies as they climbed up into the spaceship.

"Five, four, three, two, one!" called Sooty, when Sweep and Ramsbottom were safely in

their seats and holding on to them tightly. "ZERO!" the three shouted together.

Then their tummies did a very *big* swoop, for the spaceship went zooming off and away and up and along, and oh, it did all those things very quickly!

Sweep had his eyes closed firmly for the first four seconds. When he opened them, houses and clouds and birds and telegraph wires seemed to be hurrying backwards past the spaceship's viewing window.

Sooty sat in front of the switches and dials and levers, doing his best to steer the *Moonship Sooty* towards the Moon. "I think we're nicely on course!" he cried, twiddling a dial and flipping a lever. "By my reckoning we should be there in about two and a half days."

"*Days!*" gasped Ramsbottom. "Why, that's a very long time, Sooty—I didn't

have much of a breakfast, and I'm going to be jolly hungry before even two and a half *hours* are past."

Sooty and Sweep smiled.

"You don't have to worry about missing any meals as long as I've got my magic wand, Ramsbottom," beamed Sooty. "In fact, I think that right now we'll have a splendid big . . . BUMP!"

The friends found themselves lying on the floor.

That BUMP was the BUMP the spaceship made as it landed rather BUMPILY.

"What a quick ride," said Sweep, "I expect you made the spaceship go faster than you thought it could go, Sooty."

Opening the spaceship door, the friends stepped out into a rather grey, strange, quiet world. The ground seemed to be made of dusty concrete. Alongside what seemed to be ancient bricks were some old planks of wood, and some sand.

"How exciting!" gasped Ramsbottom. "We're the first people to get to the Moon in three minutes, *and* the first people to discover real sand and wooden planks there!"

"We'll be famous!" cried Sweep. "Let's take some of these things back with us!"

Just then, a very *un*moon-like workman came into view, trundling a wheelbarrow.

"Hands off that timber!" he shouted. "And get that

silly great machine out of here—we can't build a block of flats with one of those contraptions in the way!"

Sooty felt like blushing. In fact, he did blush, and his face turned rather pink.

"Oh dearie me," he gulped, "I'm afraid my spaceship steering isn't very good. This isn't the Moon at all, is it? It's that new building site about a mile down the road from our very own house, Sweep. That's where we've landed!"

Ramsbottom and Sweep burst into roars of laughter.

"Perhaps we'll just take a trip back to my house for a nice long look at my Moon poster," grinned Ramsbottom. And after Sooty had made the spaceship small enough to carry, the three friends travelled *quite* fast to Ramsbottom's house—in a friendly red bus!

Soo's Sketch-Around Shapes

SOO loves making funny drawing shapes in this fun-to-do way. She just uses all sorts of things she has in her house—scissors, rolling pin,

"Here are some sketches I have just made. Now see if you can copy them, *and* make up lots more of your very own."

plates, matchboxes, coins, pastry-cutters, toys—*anything* which she can easily draw around when the article is put on to a sheet of paper.

"Just hold it down firmly and sketch around it with a pencil or crayon," says Soo.

Happy Holiday!

SOO loves taking holiday photographs, especially when she and her friends go to the sunny seaside.

Here she is taking a photograph of Kipper. Kipper is so proud of the big sandcastle he made. Butch wants to see it, too, but the donkey he is riding seems to be going rather too fast to listen to what Butch is saying to it!

Look at the photograph Soo took. It has been made into a nice slide, and Soo is showing it to her friends on her projector.

"Just as I was going to take the photograph, something really rather funny happened, as you can see! *Do* please colour the picture so that you look at it brightly," chuckles Soo.

SOOTY'S POSTER SHOP

SOOTY sells such jolly posters in his Sootyville Poster Shop. The pictures on the posters are just the sort of pictures you would like to have in *your* room. "To see clearly what these three poster pictures are, just join the numbered dots with a pencil," says Sooty. "See how quickly and neatly you can do it!"

The pictures on the posters show: a spaceship, a pretty flower, and Sooty himself.

'Make these two Funny Snakes' says Ramsbottom

RAMSBOTTOM says it is easy to make two snaky folk like these! For the first one, draw a spiral shape on a piece of coloured paper, and then cut along the line. Hang the "snake" by cotton from the ceiling (a small piece of sticky tape will do the job), and then watch it twist and turn snakily.

With one or two carrots and some strong thread, you can soon make another bendy snake. Cut the carrot into sections with a kitchen knife, and then use a large needle to thread thick cotton through the middle of it. "Anchor" the cotton with a fat knot at both ends.

Draw on a funny face, or stick it on with pieces of coloured paper!

Easter in Sootyville

1. Sweep had such a pretty home-made greeting card from Soo, one morning. It was a HAPPY EASTER card. "It's Easter Sunday tomorrow," gasped Sweep, "I'll buy Soo an Easter Egg!"

2. Out of the house dashed Sweep. "I'll buy Soo the biggest egg ever," he thought, as he ran to the shops. "It will have pretty silvery paper around it, and chocolate buttons *in* it."

3. But Sweep was in for a surprise. For when he reached the sweetshop, there were no big eggs. There were not any Easter Eggs at all. Every Easter Egg had been sold, you see.

4. "Oh dearie dear," sighed Sweep, as he walked away rather sadly. "Now I can't give Soo the Easter surprise I wanted to." Suddenly Sweep saw a balloon seller, who gave him an idea.

5. "I'd like to buy your best, biggest balloon, please!" beamed Sweep. Just look at the big yellow balloon Sweep bought. It floats along behind Sweep *so* nicely as he hurries home with it.

6. As soon as Sweep *was* home, he got out his paints, and painted a big bow on that balloon. Then he wrapped it in silvery oven foil. It did look like an Easter Egg, didn't it?

7. Sweep *was* proud of his home-made Easter Egg. "I'll show it to Sooty on the way round to Soo's house," he said to himself. And he scampered happily towards Sooty's back gate.

8. The funny pup did not notice that Sooty was bending over just by the gate. Sooty was collecting eggs from the chicken house in his back garden. "Oops!" said Sweep, tripping over him.

9. POP! Sweep fell over on his air-filled Easter Surprise, which exploded very noisily. Sooty had such a surprise that the eggs he was carrying flew up into the air.

10. Clever Sooty managed to catch those eggs, though. When Sweep was able to tell him what had happened, and why, Sooty just smiled. "Don't worry, I've just had an idea," he said.

11. Sooty led the way indoors, carrying the chicken's eggs. Soon they were on the kitchen table, along with Sooty's paints and brushes. "We'll colour these eggs for Soo!" Sooty smiled.

12. And Sooty started to paint the eggs in such a merry way. "They won't be made of chocolate, but Soo will still be able to eat them," chuckled Sooty. Sweep joined in the egg-painting.

13. Look at the jolly way Sooty and Sweep coloured the five eggs. Don't they look smart? Sweep did not start his first egg off too well, so he washed the paint off, and began again.

14. Do you like the striped egg, or the gold and purple one best? "You can have lots of fun painting eggs when Easter comes," says Sooty to *you.* "They make nice presents for people!"

15. Soo was the happiest bear in Sootyville when Sweep and Sooty took those eggs round to her the next morning. "Happy Easter, Soo!" said Sweep and Sooty. "A Happy Easter!" replied Soo.

16. "I'd like to keep my pretty eggs for days and days," beamed Soo. "But I've just boiled and coloured some for breakfast. *Do* join me." What a happy Easter breakfast the friends had then!

LOOK AT SOOTY AND ALL HIS FRIENDS...

SOOTY and his friends are dressed in outfits which match up with the pictures on the other page!

"Say which person is ready to drive or be driven in which machine," smiles Sooty to you. "Mine is the machine which zooms through the sky —which one would *you* like?"

...AND THEIR MACHINES

Pilot Sooty goes with the aeroplane,
Fireman Butch with the fire engine,
Milkman Kipper with the milk float,
Sailor Sweep with the submarine, and
"Clippie" Soo with the bus.

Sooty's Tall T.V.!

JUST look at Sooty's funny tall T.V. set. Sooty, Butch and Kipper have fun watching the tall pictures on the tall screen. *You* can have fun, too, by using a pencil to shade in all the parts of the screen which are dotted—for then you will see the picture that the three friends can see!

"The control knobs all look the same, don't they?" says Sooty. "But the one that is slightly different is the one that changes the programme. Please tell us which one it is."

It is the bottom knob on the right.

Sweep's Amazing Magic Lino!

1. Sweep had asked Soo and Sooty round to dinner. "It's curry, and it's ready to serve!" he said. "I *am* hungry," smiled Soo. So was Sooty.

2. *Splash!* Sweep did not get as far as his friends with that delicious dinner. He tripped, and most of the food went on the floor. *Splosh!*

3. Sweep was so sad. He had no curry foods left to cook another with. "Your worn-out lino tripped you," said Soo, showing him patchy, poking-up parts.

4. At Sooty's suggestion, they all went to the shops, to buy curry things *and* lino. "We'll help you cook and lay some new lino, Sweep!" he smiled.

5. What smart new lino Sweep bought. "How bright and gay my kitchen will look now," he said, and he and Sooty started to carry that heavy roll home.

6. It was hard work carrying that heavy lino, and the friends needed lots of sit-downs. "Oh dear, I've forgotten the curry things," gasped Sweep.

7. "I think we need help — magic help!" beamed Sooty. He took his magic wand from his pocket. Soon the lino started to unroll so *Izzy-whizzily!*

8. "All aboard the Magic Lino!" Sooty called. Three seconds later, the friends were whizzing skywards. "Where are we going?" gasped Sweep.

9. Those friends soon found out. The Magic Lino took them to India! "We'll land and have a lovely curry," shouted Sooty. "And then we'll fly home again, and fix this new lino in your kitchen for you!" And that's what they did.

Lawn Fishing

SOOTY and his friends like fishing with magnets! But just look at the twisty tangles the fishing lines are in.

Sooty, Sweep, Soo, Ramsbottom, Kipper and Butch are not sure which fisherman has "caught" which metal fish. "Please look along the maze of fishing lines, and tell us who has caught the blue fish, who has caught the green fish, and who has caught the red fish," says Sooty. "And say which three fishermen haven't caught any fish at all!"

Soo has caught the blue fish, Sooty the green fish, and Sweep the red fish, haven't they? It's Kipper, Butch and Ramsbottom who haven't had a "catch"!

Paper Handies

THESE two hand puppets of Sooty and Sweep are so easy to make—from paper!

If you don't want to cut this page, use tracing paper to copy these two puppet shapes of Sooty and Sweep on to paper which has been doubled over. Give your drawings gay colours.

Cut around the edge so that you have two same-sized puppet shapes for each puppet. Sticky tape them together. When you slide them over your hand, your three middle fingers go into the head part, and your smallest finger and thumb fit into the arms.

"Now *you* can give a merry puppet show!" laughed Sweep and Sooty.

Sooty Helps Soo with the Spring Cleaning

"RINGLE-DINGLE" went Sooty Bear's doorbell one sunny afternoon.

Sooty hurried to the door to open it, for he likes having visitors very much indeed. There on the doorstep was Soo Bear.

"Do come in, Soo," smiled Sooty, politely helping Soo to take her coat off. "You're just in time," he went on, "to come out into the garden and help me make a sand-speed-boat in the sandpit. We can splash some water around it when it's finished, to make it look just like a real boat!"

Soo is usually the first person to join in any fun-to-do game. So Sooty was quite surprised when she just sat there in Sooty's comfiest chair.

"I don't feel like playing in the sandpit this afternoon, thank you," sighed the pretty little bear.

"Why *ever* not?" asked Sooty.

"I'm just rather tired, that's all," said Soo. "I'm Spring Cleaning my house from top to bottom, you see, and it's jolly hard work."

She stood up, and put her coat on. "I'd better pop back straight away," she said, "because if I don't, I'll just never get it all finished. Good-bye, Sooty!"

Soo was halfway up the garden path to the gate before Sooty caught up with her. "Hey, Soo," he said, "you don't have to do all that work by yourself—I'll be pleased to come along and give you a hand!"

Soo looked pleased then, too!

She looked even *more* pleased when Sooty ran into the house, and came back holding a vacuum cleaner. "That *will* be a help to get the carpets clean, Sooty," said Soo.

"It certainly will," replied

Sooty. "But first of all we'll get it to do another sort of job for us," From his pocket, Sooty took a short piece of wood which is the most precious thing he possesses. It is no ordinary piece of wood – it is a *magic* piece. Yes, it is his magic *wand!*

"Izzy-whizzy, helper be – travel fast for Soo and me!" said Sooty, making sure that he and Soo had their legs across that vacuum cleaner first. Can you guess what happened next? Yes, that vacuum cleaner zoomed forward rather like a funny jet plane, with Soo and Sooty riding it. How the folk of Sootyville stared and laughed to see that vacuum jet speeding along about two feet above the ground with its laughing passengers.

Soon the two friends were in Soo's very own kitchen; the vacuum cleaner was standing quietly by the stairs. "I feel better already after that exciting ride," beamed Soo, putting on an apron. Sooty put one on too.

"Right, where shall we start?" asked Sooty.

"I've done most of the upstairs rooms," replied Soo, "but the paintwork on the stairs and the banisters needs a good wash."

"That's just the job for Sooty," said Sooty, fetching water and detergent in a packet, and a cloth, and setting to work. He felt so full of energy that he did not use any magic to help him – not even to get the rather-hard-to-clean paintwork white where it was extra-grey and grimy.

When that job was done and the paint looked sparkly-as-new, he went to Soo and asked what he could do next.

"I think we'll take all the loose carpets and rugs out-

side and give them a good beating, to get all the dust out of them," smiled Soo. "Watch out you don't get dusty yourself, Sooty."

Sooty didn't get dusty.

After he had carried two heavy green carpets and a red rug out on to the lawn, he held his magic wand in his hand, and made some magic

which had those carpets leaping into the air and flopping over a strong clothes line! The two sticks that Sooty *izzy-whizzily* magicked did all the carpet beating for him in a very *whacky* way!

So much dust came out of those carpets and the rug that Soo said she had never ever seen them looking so clean. She and Sooty watched it all taking place from a very *un*dusty stool seat in the kitchen, enjoying a cup of tea, at the same time.

"I've been vacuum cleaning the living room with your nice vacuun cleaner," said Soo, pouring *another* cup of tea for her friend. "*And* I've dusted away all the dust on top of the pelmets. So all that's left to do is wash the curtains and give the hall a thorough going over."

The curtains were quite an easy job. But when Soo and Sooty took the small table out of the hall, and the two pictures from the walls, *and* the umbrella stand from the corner, the friends gave each other rather glum looks.

"H'm," said Sooty.

"Oh dear," said Soo, looking around her. "It isn't just a Spring Cleaning job which is needed here—it's a decorating job, I'm afraid."

Sooty's answer was to take Soo by the hand, and lead her to a living room chair.

Soo wondered what was happening!

Sooty fetched paint brushes, wallpaper, wallpaper paste, and paint, from the cupboard under the stairs, and put all the things on the floor in the middle of the hall. Then he joined Soo in a comfy rocking chair right next to her.

Holding his magic wand out in front of him, he said rather loudly: *"Izzy-whizzy, work for Soo – make the hall as good as new!"*

How amazing it was to see those paint brushes leap to life, and start painting.

How funny it was to see the paste brush slip-slapping wallpaper paste on to the back of the wallpaper – and then see the wallpaper fly flip-flappily into the air, and move forward to stick itself against the wall so neatly.

"It's better than being at a lovely show!" said Soo happily. "Thank you very much, Sooty."

"It's a pleasure, Soo," smiled Sooty.

He really is a *very* helpful bear.